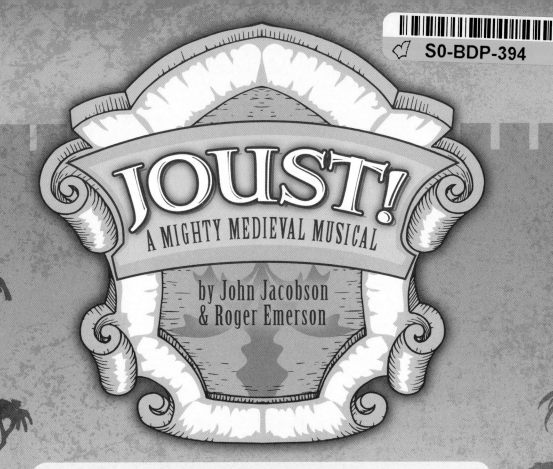

JOUST!
A MIGHTY MEDIEVAL MUSICAL

by John Jacobson
& Roger Emerson

TABLE OF CONTENTS

Musical Performance Rights

HAL•LEONARD®
CORPORATION

7777 W. BLUEMOUND RD. P.O. BOX 13819 MILWAUKEE, WI 53213

Visit Hal Leonard Online at
www.halleonard.com

1. MIGHTY MEDIEVAL MEN

Words and Music by JOHN JACOBSON
and ROGER EMERSON

MERLIN: *(spoken directly to audience, over music introduction)* Once upon a medieval time, in a land far away, unless, of course, you are in England, then it's not so far away at all, there lived a mighty King, who had a son by the name of Arthur, that he did not want. He gave that son away to his mystical advisor, Merlin. That's me, and I, in turn, gave the King's son to serve the good knight Sir Hector, as his lowly page, and then, squire. Sir Hector and Arthur lived in a place crowded with the most rowdy, bawdy, unruly, untidy, yet . . . MIGHTY MEDIEVAL MEN!

3

4

men!_____ We are the lords of chiv - al - ry!_____ We are

might-y me - di - eval men! We are the lords of chiv - al -

ry!_____ We are might-y me - di - eval men!

They think they're might - y hot, but

some - how they for - got, the wom - en are the ones who rule the

day! No dam - sels in dis - tress as we clean up their mess, and

yet we have to hear as they pro - claim! We are

awe - some! They are flight - y! And we know they can fight an - y-

6

STOP RECORDING

SCENE 1 *(Minstrel musicians continue to play.)*

Merlin: *(to musicians)* Very nice… very nice. Okay… Okay. *(He's had enough.)* We get it! *(Musicians stop playing and exit.)(Merlin turns to the audience and continues.)* You all know the King Arthur legend. If not, let me tell you …

Lady Luck: Oh, Merlin, let us tell it. You'll go on for days!

Merlin: *(a bit flustered)* Well, I guess that would be all right. But I …

Lady Bird: *(interrupting him)* It was the day of the big joust. All of the knights were gathered in the roped-off area, with their armor, horses, weapons, …

Lady Bug: And attended by their young squires.

Lady Sadie: Squires are young men who hope one day to be knights themselves.

Lady Singalot: The squires do everything for the knights, including getting them ready for the joust.

Merlin: Remember, Arthur was the squire for Sir Hector.

(The Damsels get more and more excited.)

Lady Humalong: Everyone is gathered for the biggest joust of the year!

Lady Luck: It's like the World Series of all Jousts!

Lady Bird: The Stanley Cup!

Lady Sadie: The Super Bowl!

Lady Singalot: The Olympics of the jousting world!

Merlin: Enough already. Let's have a song.

START RECORDING
SONG 2: JOUST!

2. JOUST!

Words and Music by JOHN JACOBSON
and ROGER EMERSON

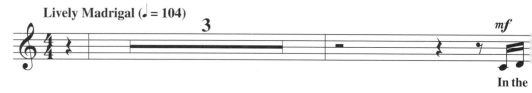

In the

ver - y month of May from near and far a - way, the

la - dies and the no - ble knights make this a spe - cial day. Come and

see the sport of kings, of gal - lant of - fer - ings. We

try to knock one off his horse, then ev - 'ry - bod - y sings! With a

hey and a ho and a non - ny no,   ev - 'ry knight can play! With a
(nah - nee)

hey and a ho and a non - ny no,   on this joust - ing day! With a

10

hey and a ho and a non-ny no, ev-'ry knight can play! With a

hey and a ho and a non-ny no, on this joust-ing day! With a

hey and a ho and a non-ny no, rac-ing to and fro! With a

hey and a ho and a non-ny no, a joust-ing we will, we will,

we will, we will go! On guard!

STOP RECORDING

SCENE 2

(Minstrel musicians enter. They play a few notes.)

Merlin: *(to musicians)* Enough already! Stop! *(Musicians stop playing, hang their heads and exit.) (to the audience)* Now, where was I? Oh yes. It was the squire's job to serve his knight. So what happens when the knight forgets his most important weapon?

Arthur: The squire has to get it!

Lady Grady: Sir Hector forgot his sword at home.

Lady Cute: Not good for a knight who is on deck at the Joust.

Merlin: So, Arthur takes off as fast as his squire-y legs will take him.

Lady Clever: He runs through the streets of town, past the castle moat!

Lady Lahdee: Past the church and several fine dining establishments.

Lady Dah: By the time he reaches the town square, he realizes he is only half way home.

Lady Dee Dee: He knows he will never make it all the way home, get Sir Hector's sword and then get back to the Joust in time for Sir Hector to participate!

Merlin: Now, this is where I have to remind you of the legend of King Arthur. You will recall from your lessons that when the king (Arthur's father) died, there was no heir to the throne.

Lady Tweedle: That'll teach him to give his son away!

Merlin: So, the royal court had a sword placed in a stone in the town square.

Lady Twiddle: The legend says that whomever could pull that sword out of the stone would be the rightful heir to the throne.

Lady Tweedle: They would become the king!

Lady Twiddle: *(annoyed)* I just said that.

Merlin: It is in front of this sword-stabbed stone that Squire Arthur finds himself, as he's racing home to retrieve Sir Hector's sword.

Lady Luck: What you probably don't recall from this famous legend, is that only a few steps away from THAT stone, was another rock.

Lady Bird: And sticking out of THAT rock was something even more beautiful and enticing than the former king's sword.

Merlin: And THAT'S what caught Arthur's attention.

(Arthur is standing between the two stones. One has a sword sticking out of it. The other – a Boomwhacker.)

Arthur: Hmmm. Two stones. Each with something interesting protruding from it. I only have time to choose one and get back to the Joust. Hmmm… *(He looks back and forth.)* … *(looking at the sword)* Well, this one is most certainly a sword and seems the logical choice. *(looking at the Boomwhacker)* But this one is much more colorful and seems full of many fantastic possibilities. Hmmm…*(He grabs the Boomwhacker. All onlookers gasp!)* I'm taking this one! *(It slides easily out of the stone. He looks at it curiously and then runs back the way he came from, waving the Boomwhacker high, like a sword.)*

Merlin: *(to the audience)* Does this sound at all familiar to you? Well, watch what happens next.

Arthur: *(to Sir Hector and the other Medieval Men)* My Lord! My Lord! I have brought you the best instrument that I could find! Isn't it colorful?

Sir Hector: What!? What is this?

Arthur: I have no idea, but isn't it beautiful?

Sir Hector: Beautiful, indeed! But what can it do?

Sir Tinly: It is the strange tube that was sticking out of the stone in the town square. Everyone knows that whomever pulls it out is the rightful heir to the throne.

Sir Real: I thought that was the sword.

Sir Prize: Duh! It works for both.

All: All hail the king! All hail King Arthur! *(all kneel)*

Arthur: Wow! Am I really the new king? Can it really be?

Sir Round: You're it, Your Majesty. Now, what will be your first decree?

Arthur: You mean … anything?

Sir Vent: Sure! You're the king.

Arthur: *(thinks)* Well … then I decree that from now on in this kingdom, there will be no more use for swords or weapons of any sort, except this marvelous, colorful instrument.

All Knights: *(shocked)* WHAT?? You can't be serious!

Lady Bug: I think it's a marvelous idea.

(All the women agree.)

Lady Sadie: And until you men get used to the idea, none of us Damsels are going to be friendly to you at all.

Lady Singalot: Or wash your clothes …

Lady Humalong: Or cook your meals …

Lady Grady: Or cheer your jousting.

Lady Cute: King Arthur says "no more swords."

All Women: And that's the way it's going to be!

Men: *(despondently)* All hail the king.

START RECORDING
SONG 3: THAT'S THE WAY IT'S GOING TO BE
(featuring the Damsels)

3. THAT'S THE WAY IT'S GOING TO BE

Words and Music by JOHN JACOBSON
and ROGER EMERSON

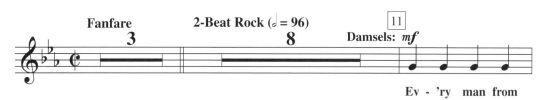

34

That's the way it's gon - na be! _____

38

Mark my words and you will see: _____

subito p

42

That's the way it's gon - na be!

Sir Lee: But wait a minute. You mean, after I come home from a long day of lording over the serfs, you're not going to have a hot meal waiting for me?

7

50 **Lady Clever:** Not if you're "lording" with anything but that! *(pointing to Boomwhacker)*

4

Sir Duke: You mean, I'm going to have to wash my own clothes every year?

Lady Lahdee: Or wear them dirty!

Sir Ender: You mean, I have to milk my own cow?

Lady Dah: From now on, unless you pick up that Boomwhacker instead of a sword, if you want milk, you get mooooo-ving!

Arthur: Boomwhacker? What a fantastic name!

All MMM: Argh!!!!

Lord Dance-Alot: Come on, we've got to get this sword out of here. uuuuHHH! *(He fails.)*

(repeat as needed)

58 **Sir Vival:** Here, let me try! *(much grunting)* Ooooh. *(holding his back)* I think I pulled something!

62

STOP RECORDING

SCENE 3

Merlin: Now, it all seemed fine until, rumor has it, there was an attack coming from France.

Messenger: *(running in)* Your Majesty! Rumor has it, there is an attack coming from France.

Merlin: I just said that.

Arthur: An attack from France? Oh no!

Sir Up: And all we have to fight with are these colorful Boomwhackers!

(The men start discussing loudly amongst themselves the terrible state of their affairs.)

Arthur: Stop! Silence! We must keep sound heads or we will surely go down in defeat!

Sir Reptitious: But, Your Majesty, what are we to do?

Arthur: I think we should sing . . . a round.

All Men: What!!?

Arthur: I mean, rounds are good. Here, gather 'round my <u>round</u> table and I'll show you what I mean.

START RECORDING

SONG 4: ROUND OF THE ROUND TABLE

4. ROUND OF THE ROUND TABLE

Words and Music by JOHN JACOBSON
and ROGER EMERSON

Arthur: Now, are we boys, or are we men?
MMM: Men!
Arthur: Are we men or are we knights?
MMM: Knights!
Arthur: Are we knights of the Round Table?
MMM: Yes, Your Majesty!
Arthur: Then sing, men, sing! Like the knights you are!

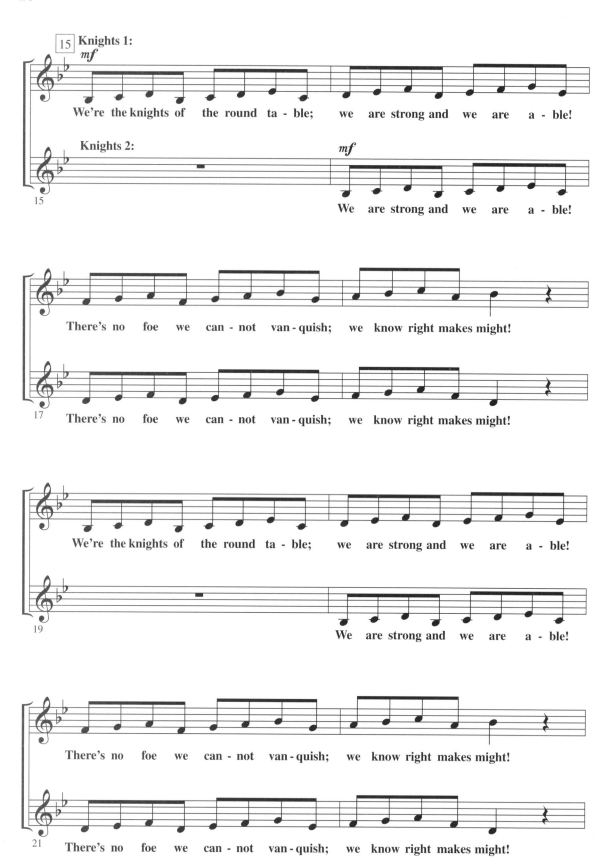

Damsels:
(shout)
LEFT!

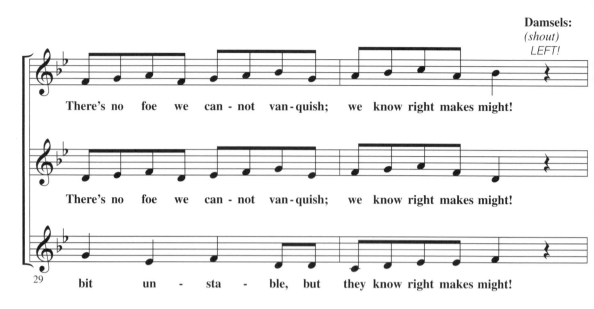

There's no foe we can-not van-quish; we know right makes might!

There's no foe we can-not van-quish; we know right makes might!

bit un - sta - ble, but they know right makes might!

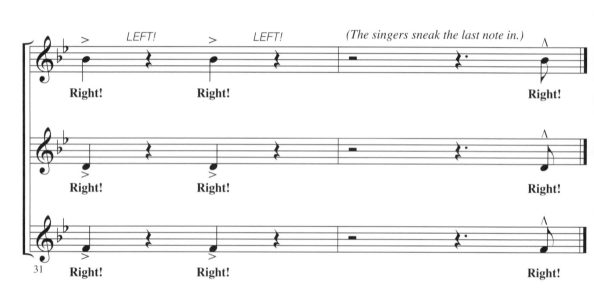

LEFT! *LEFT!* *(The singers sneak the last note in.)*

Right! Right! Right!

Right! Right! Right!

Right! Right! Right!

STOP RECORDING

SCENE 4

Arthur: There, wasn't that nice?

Sir Rah: Okay, Your Majesty, we're doing our best, but we still don't know what to do with these things. *(holds up a Boomwhacker)*

Arthur: I know! Let's call in the smartest advisors we know. They'll know what to do.

Merlin: I, naturally, thought the king was referring to me. But as I stepped forward, I heard …

Sir Indipitous: Yes! Call in the court jesters! They always know what to do.

Sir Face: IF you can get past their silly jokes and ridiculous songs!

Sir Duke: Look! I see one now … a fool on the hill!

Sir Vival: Not just one, but a whole cast of them.

START RECORDING

SONG 5: NOBODY'S FOOL

5. NOBODY'S FOOL

Words and Music by JOHN JACOBSON
and ROGER EMERSON

Lively (♩ = 152)

5
The smart - est dudes in-
care - ful who you

7
side the court; they're cute and kind - a cool.
call a fool, they may be sly like fox.

11
They're al - ways called as last re - sort,
With no ex - cep - tion to the rule,

16
'cause they did well in school.
they think out - side the box.

21 cresc.
20
Nev - er dull, nev - er cruel,

25
they're no - bod - y's fool! No, no no! They're no-

(pickup, 1st time only) mf
30
bod - y's fool! Be

(Spoken solo, one-liner joke)
"No one but a fool is always right!"

STOP RECORDING

SCENE 5

Jester 1: Your Majesty, we hear you have a problem.

Arthur: Yes, my friend. I have made the decision that we will be a peace-loving nation; that we will turn our swords into Boomwhackers and live side by side with our neighbors in friendship.

Lady Dee Dee: And we damsels are backing him up by not being nice to the men until they go along with the king.

All Damsels: That's the way it's going to be.

Jester 2: I think that sounds like a great idea!

Sir Hector: The problem is … we have just been told that the French are on their way to attack us, and I don't think they are going to be armed with only "Boomwhackers"!

Arthur: It's all my fault. I truly believed we wouldn't need weapons if we always did the right thing, and worked for a land filled with harmony. And now, I've put my entire kingdom in jeopardy.

START RECORDING

SONG 6: ALL I EVER WANTED

6. ALL I EVER WANTED

Words and Music by JOHN JACOBSON
and ROGER EMERSON

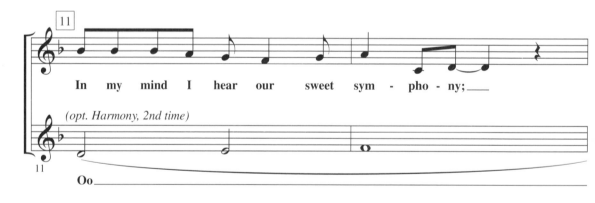

STOP RECORDING

SCENE 6

Merlin: The French soldiers landed on the shore of the kingdom.

Messenger: The French are coming! The French are coming!

Merlin: *(annoyed)* I just said that.

(All the men start panicking and saying things like "What are we going to do?" "All we have are Boomwhackers!" "We're doomed!" etc.)

 (Then the French arrive, soldiers and ladies. The soldiers are all carrying recorders and playing the notes B, A, G over and over, or use Track 18" French Arrival" on the CD.)

Arthur: What? Can this really be? Did you really arrive with only those instruments?

French King: *(with a French accent)* Oui, monsier. There was one of these sticking out of a rock in the middle of Paris, and now our ladies have insisted that we turn our swords into these or they will not be nice to us.

French Lady Gigi: Or wash your clothes …

French Lady Fifi: Or cook your meals …

French Lady CeeCee: Or cheer your jousting …

French Soldier 1: *(looking at Boomwhacker)* I see you have your own problems to worry about.

French Soldier 2: They are colorful, though.

Sir Up: Well, what are we going to do?

Arthur: Think! I have to think! *(He starts tapping his Boomwhacker on the ground mindlessly.)*

Merlin: And then something very special began to happen.

START RECORDING

SONG 7: WE'RE MAKIN' MUSIC

7. WE'RE MAKIN' MUSIC

Words and Music by JOHN JACOBSON
and ROGER EMERSON

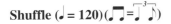

Arthur: *(spoken over the music)* Yes! Yes! My countrymen! My friends! Lend me your ears! This is what I was talking about!

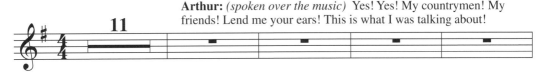

(Arthur) Music! Harmony! Having might by being right! Being in tune! I knew that if we all just tried a little harder, we could put away our weapons forever . . .

(Arthur) and make beautiful music. Listen! Listen! We are doing it! We are making music together! And it is beautiful!

(Arthur) My people, from this day forward, let us never forget this sound and this moment ... the moment when men and women

(Arthur) put down their swords and shields, picked up a somewhat musical instrument, raised their voices and sang! ... Sing, boy, siiiiiiiing!!

40

f

Nah nah nah nah nah Non-ny non-ny no!   Nah nah nah nah nah Non-ny non-ny no!

f

40   One   by   one,   we're mak in'

Nah nah nah   nah nah Non-ny non-ny no! We're   mak - in'   mu - sic!

42   mu - sic!

Nah nah nah nah nah Non-ny non-ny no!   Nah nah nah nah nah Non-ny non-ny no!

44   One   by   one,   we're mak-in'

Song ends abruptly

Nah nah nah   nah nah Non-ny non-ny no! We're   mak - in'   mu - sic!

46   mu - sic!

STOP RECORDING

Messenger: Your Majesty! Your Majesty! I have terrible news! The men of Scotland are invading from the north and are sure to overrun us all!!

 (All gasp and then are silent as the sounds of Scottish bagpipes are heard from off stage. If performing live, play 4 half notes of open 5ths – G and D below middle C. If performing with CD, use Track 20 for short bagpipe excerpt.)

All: *(to the audience)* Bagpipes? No problem!!!

START RECORDING

REPRISE: WE'RE MAKIN' MUSIC

8. REPRISE: WE'RE MAKIN' MUSIC

Words and Music by JOHN JACOBSON
and ROGER EMERSON

9. CURTAIN CALL: MIGHTY MEDIEVAL MEN

**Words and Music by JOHN JACOBSON
and ROGER EMERSON**